My Naughty Little S Goes Fishing

Dorothy Edwards &
Shirley Hughes

LITTLE
MAMMOTH

A long time ago, when I was a little girl,
I had a sister who was very much younger
than me. Although my sister was often naughty,
most of the naughty things she did were
so funny that no one was cross with her
for very long and she made a lot of friends.

Here is a story about one of my sister's
adventures. It is called My Naughty
Little Sister Goes Fishing.

One day, when I was a little girl, and my sister was a very little girl, some children came to our house and asked my mother if I could go fishing with them.

They had jam-jars with string on them, and fishing-nets and sandwiches and lemonade.

My mother said "Yes" – I could go with them; and she found *me* a jam-jar and a fishing-net and cut *me* some sandwiches.

Then my naughty little sister said, "I want to go! I want to go!" Just like that. So my mother said I might as well take her too.

Then my mother cut some sandwiches for my little sister,
but she didn't give her a jam-jar or a fishing-net because
she said she was too little to go near the water. My
mother gave my little sister a basket to put some stones in,
because my little sister liked to pick up stones, and she
gave me a big bottle of lemonade for both of us.

My mother said, "You mustn't let your little sister get
herself wet. You must keep her away from the water."

And I said, "All right, Mother, I promise."

So then we set off to the little river, and we took our shoes off and our socks off and tucked up our clothes and we went into the water to catch fish with our fishing-nets, and we filled our jam-jars with water to put the fishes in when we caught them. And we said to my naughty little sister, "You mustn't come, you'll get yourself wet."

Well, we paddled and paddled and fished and fished,
but we didn't catch any fish at all, not one little tiny one
even. Then a boy said, "Look, there is your sister in the
water too!"

And, do you know, my naughty little sister had walked right into the water with her shoes and socks on, and she was trying to fish with her little basket.

I said, "Get out of the water," and she said, "No."
 I said, "Get out at once," and she said,
"I don't want to."
 I said, "You'll get all wet," and she said,
"I don't care."

Wasn't she naughty?

So I said, "I must fetch you out then," and my naughty
little sister tried to run away in the water which was a
silly thing to do because she fell down and got all wet.

She got her frock wet, and her petticoat wet, and
her knickers wet, and her vest wet, and her hair wet,
and her hair-ribbons – all soaking wet. Of course,
I told you her shoes and socks were wet before.

And she cried and cried.

So we fetched her out of the water, and we said,
"Oh dear, she will catch a cold," and we took off
her wet frock, and her wet petticoat and her
wet knickers and her wet vest, and her wet hair-ribbons,
and her wet shoes and socks, and we hung all the things
to dry on the bushes in the sunshine, and we wrapped
my naughty little sister up in a woolly cardigan.

My little sister *cried and cried*.

So we gave her the sandwiches, and she ate them all up.
She ate up her sandwiches and my sandwiches, and
the other children's sandwiches all up – and she cried
and cried.

Then we gave her the lemonade and she spilled it all over the grass, and she cried and cried.

Then one of the children gave her an apple, and another of the children gave her some toffees, and, while she was eating these, we took her clothes off the bushes and ran about with them in the sunshine until they were dry

When her clothes were quite dry, we put them all back on her again, and she screamed and screamed because she didn't want her clothes on any more.

So I took her home, and my mother said, "Oh, you've let your little sister fall into the water."

And I said, "How do you know? Because we dried all her clothes," and my mother said, "Ah, but you didn't *iron* them." My little sister's clothes were all crumpled and messy.

Then my mother said I
should not have any sugary
biscuits for supper because I
was disobedient. Only bread
and butter, and she said my
little sister must go straight to
bed, and have some hot milk
to drink.

And my mother said to my little sister, "Don't you think you were a naughty little girl to go in the water?"

And my naughty little sister said, "I won't do it any more because it was too wet."

But, do you know, when my mother went to throw
away the stones out of my little sister's basket, she
found a little fish in the bottom, which my naughty
little sister had caught!

First published in Great Britain 1952 as 'Going Fishing' in *My Naughty Little Sister*
This edition first published in 1976 by Methuen Children's Books Ltd
Reprinted 1978, 1979, 1983, 1985
First published 1980, Reprinted 1980, 1983, 1985
First published 1989 by Little Mammoth
an imprint of Mandarin Paperbacks, Michelin House, 81 Fulham Road, London SW3 6RB
Reprinted 1990 (twice)
Text copyright © 1976 Dorothy Edwards, Illustrations copyright © 1976 Shirley Hughes
ISBN 0 7497 0124 2
Printed in Great Britain by Scotprint Ltd, Musselburgh